STARTER
Vocabula

CW00347031

in
English

PETER VINEY
KAREN VINEY

OXFORD
UNIVERSITY PRESS

Contents

Word games

in
English

International words

Underline the words that are the same in your language. (Circle) the words
that are *nearly* the same.

pizza	computer	information	hotel
spaghetti	program	police	café
sandwich	telephone	taxi	buffet
pasta	CD	accommodation	restaurant
omelette	DVD	parking	trattoria
croissant	television	university	bistro
espresso	radio	college	discotheque
cappuccino	cassette	hospital	club
burger	minidisc		bar
hot dog			pub
cola			
tuna	saxophone	airport	
lemon	synthesizer	departures	
	percussion	check-in	
	guitar	bank	
	violin	exchange	
	cello	bureau	
	bass	arrivals	
	orchestra	passport control	

Alphabet

Make an alphabet table, e.g. *X – X Files   Z – zoo*.
You can use international words (*pizza*), or English names (*Peter*),
or places (*Paris*).

A B C D E F G

H I J K L M N

O P Q R S T U

V W X Y Z

Spell your name on the telephone, e.g. *Dan – D for dog, A for apple,*
N for no.

Films (1)

Underline the countries in these film titles. Circle the nationalities.

1	The English Patient	7	The Italian Job
2	From Russia With Love	8	Congo
3	The French Connection	9	Big Trouble In Little China
4	The Mexican	10	A Passage To India
5	Prince Of Egypt	11	Zorba The Greek
6	The Boys From Brazil	12	Once Upon A Time In America

Find the words

0	1	2	3	4	5	6	7	8	9
M	I	R	E	N	U	B	H	A	S

e.g. seven   three   two = *her*

1 four eight zero three
2 seven one nine
3 four five two nine three
4 nine seven three

5 zero two nine
6 seven three
7 four five zero six three two

Plurals

Circle the correct spelling in each line.

keies	keys	keyz
watchis	watches	watchs
photos	photoes	phottos
dictionarys	dictionares	dictionaries
toothbrushs	toothbrushes	teethbrushes
librarys	librares	libraries
strawberries	strawberies	strawberrys
armchaires	armchairs	armchairies
factories	factores	factorys
picturs	picturres	pictures

Crossword

Complete the crossword.

Across

1 17, ..., 19, 20 (8)
5 'Good morning ....,
   good morning madam.' (3)
6 The contraction is *'m*. (2)
7 Possessive adjective. (2)
9 Plural of *man*. (3)
10 A happy colour. (6)
12 This and ....(4)

Down

1 'Anything ....?'
   'No, thanks.' (4)
2 Where is Frankfurt? (7)
3 The hot one is red. The cold one
   is blue. (3)
4 'What's your ....?'
   'Maria.' (4)
8 Opposite of *large*. (5)
11 Not *drink*. (3)

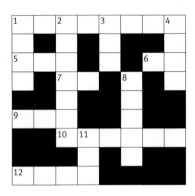

Songs (1)

A music critic said, 'The Beatles are very popular because their songs have got personal pronouns and possessive adjectives in the titles'.

Look at these song titles. Underline the subject pronouns (e.g. *she*).
Circle the object pronouns (e.g. *me*).
Put a * by the possessive adjectives (e.g. *my*).

1 She Loves You
2 I Want To Hold Your Hand
3 From Me To You
4 All You Need Is Love
5 In My Life
6 And I Love Her
7 Please Please Me
8 All My Loving
9 Can't Buy Me Love
10 We Can Work It Out

11 I Want You
12 I Feel Fine
13 With A Little Help From My friends
14 When I'm Sixty-four
15 She's Leaving Home
16 You Can't Do That
17 She's A Woman
18 Two Of Us
19 I'm So Tired
20 Martha, My Dear

Food and drink

Can you find ten food and seven drink words?

W	T	E	A	M	C	O	L	A	F
A	F	C	H	I	C	K	E	N	R
T	H	S	A	L	A	D	R	W	I
E	M	I	L	K	S	H	A	K	E
R	B	F	I	S	H	O	C	C	S
J	U	I	C	E	J	T	O	H	P
O	R	A	N	G	E	D	F	E	A
Q	G	K	A	I	V	O	F	E	S
R	E	D	Z	L	F	G	E	S	T
T	R	P	I	Z	Z	A	E	E	A

Opposites: adjectives

Match the adjectives with their opposites.

good	new
small	cold
black	fantastic
old	closed
left	bad
open	large
awful	white
hot	right

Films (2)

Have these film titles got a male or a female word in them? Write _M_ or _F_.

1 Pretty Woman
2 Three Kings
3 Uncle Buck
4 Sister Act
5 Tank Girl

6 The Lost Boys
7 The African Queen
8 The Godfather
9 Men In Black
10 Batman Forever

Which word?

**Which words do *you* think of first? Tick (✔) one example.
(All the words are correct.)**

new	☐ new potatoes ☐ New Year ☐ New York ☐ new clothes
nice	☐ a nice house ☐ a nice dinner ☐ nice people ☐ Have a nice day.
old	☐ old friends ☐ an old story ☐ old people ☐ old shoes
small	☐ small children ☐ a small whisky ☐ a small size ☐ a small town
red	☐ red wine ☐ red hair ☐ red shirts (football) ☐ the red channel (airport)
large	☐ a large size ☐ a large coffee ☐ a large car ☐ a large drink

Songs (2)

**All these songs have got an *'s* in the title.
Put 1 (*is*), 2 (*has*) or 3 (*possessive*).**

How many words? (1)

**How many words can you find? Use each letter once.
There is one nine-letter word.**

E	H	E
N	T	E
L	O	P

10 words = good

14 words = excellent

Clothes

How many clothes can you put in each box?

men only	women only	on the feet	for hot days	for cold days

Opposites: prepositions

Match the prepositions with their opposites.

in	from
up	across
on	down
to	out
along	off

Jobs

Match words from column A and column B.

A	B
police	assistant
office	officer
shop	reporter
flight	attendant
disc	worker
newspaper	jockey

Odd one out (1)

Circle the different word in each line.

dress	top	shirt	skirt
new	large	small	medium
parents	children	grandson	cousins
office	college	school	university
city	town	flat	village
street	park	road	avenue
wine	spirits	beer	soft drinks

Opposites: verbs

Match the verbs with their opposites.

pull	play
start	hate
turn on	stay in
come	push
work	go to bed
love	go
go out	turn off
get up	finish

The next word ... (1)

Tick (✓) the words that go with the verbs, e.g.

phone ✓ a friend ✓ your family ✗ a door ✓ the office

---

listen ☐ to me ☐ to the music ☐ the TV ☐ to the orchestra
☐ for you

---

read ☐ my ☐ a book ☐ a newspaper ☐ this ☐ happy

---

write ☐ a note ☐ a computer ☐ a letter ☐ to me ☐ next week

---

turn on ☐ the TV ☐ the radio ☐ the book ☐ the tap
☐ by the window

---

sit ☐ down ☐ on the armchair ☐ careful ☐ by the window

---

be ☐ careful ☐ listen ☐ quiet ☐ quick ☐ there ☐ me

Places

Match words from column A and column B.

A	B
railway	mall
public	hall
town	rank
shopping	station
taxi	box
telephone	toilet

Sports

Can you find twelve sports?

K	C	S	O	C	C	E	R	F	G
S	W	I	M	M	I	N	G	O	N
Q	B	T	D	R	H	J	O	O	E
U	A	E	G	U	K	F	L	T	T
A	S	N	X	G	A	L	F	B	B
S	E	N	T	B	R	Y	R	A	A
H	B	I	M	Y	A	I	U	L	L
B	A	S	K	E	T	B	A	L	L
Z	L	V	Q	F	E	N	S	H	J
W	L	R	U	N	N	I	N	G	P

Odd one out (2)

Circle the different word in each line.

running	swimming	walking	writing
football	tennis	reading	basketball
Indian	Spain	Italian	French
like	can	love	hate
us	they	me	him
concert	classical	rock	jazz
cinema	stadium	opera house	film

The next word ... (2)

Tick (✓) the words that go with the verbs, e.g.

phone ... ☑ a friend   ☑ your family   ☒ a door   ☑ the office

have	☐ a bath ☐ dinner ☐ a film ☐ a shower ☐ breakfast ☐ a good time ☐ a hospital
go	☐ to work ☐ a pizza ☐ to bed ☐ on holiday ☐ a station ☐ home
work	☐ at home ☐ a meal ☐ in a factory ☐ for a company ☐ in Paris ☐ a bath
live in	☐ breakfast ☐ a flat ☐ a house ☐ a small town ☐ a bed ☐ a city ☐ Florida
know	☐ some people ☐ the answer ☐ a passport ☐ them ☐ a good restaurant
meet	☐ a new car ☐ people ☐ the family ☐ tickets ☐ at 7.30 ☐ a film ☐ tomorrow

Films (3)

Look at the film titles. Underline the numbers (1, 2, 3 ...). Circle the ordinal numbers (1st, 2nd ...).

1   The Third Man
2   The Sixth Sense
3   The Fifth Element
4   Twelve Angry Men
5   The Seven Samurai
6   One Hundred And One Dalmatians
7   Six Days, Seven Nights
8   The Three Musketeers
9   The First Family
10 Four Weddings And A Funeral

How many words? (2)

**How many words can you find? Use each letter once.
There is one nine-letter word.**

L	K	I
H	M	A
E	K	S

14 words = good
20 words = excellent

The next word ... (3)

Tick (✓) the words that go with the verbs, e.g.

phone ✓ a friend   ✓ your family   ✗ a door   ✓ the office

see ☐ a film   ☐ lunch   ☐ my friends   ☐ a programme   ☐ the city

make ☐ an appointment   ☐ dinner   ☐ a mistake   ☐ an exercise
☐ football

stay ☐ in   ☐ out   ☐ at home   ☐ a CD   ☐ in a hotel   ☐ the video
☐ here   ☐ there

play ☐ exercise   ☐ tennis   ☐ gymnastics   ☐ chess   ☐ football
☐ a CD   ☐ dancing

do ☐ homework   ☐ some work   ☐ likes   ☐ a job   ☐ clothes
☐ a new car

have ☐ flu   ☐ an operation   ☐ a job   ☐ working   ☐ an idea
☐ some tea   ☐ friends

How many words? (3)

How many words can you find? Use each letter once.
There is one nine-letter word.

D	D	A
Y	W	E
E	S	N

14 words = good

20 words = excellent

Odd one out (3)

Circle the different word.

flight	plane	journey	drive
rain	snow	cloud	weather
buffet	café	restaurant	station
went	bought	like	came
shirt	new	large	small
lemon	apple	orange	potato
lunch	breakfast	coffee	dinner

Buildings

Put the words in the correct places.

building / house / hotel / cinema / farm / church / restaurant / bridge / office

The next word ... (4)

Tick (✓) the words that go with the verbs, e.g.

phone	✓ a friend ✓ your family ✗ a door ✓ the office
went	☐ a new jacket ☐ home ☐ to work ☐ to bed ☐ shopping ☐ some fries
bought	☐ tea ☐ to work ☐ a T-shirt ☐ a sandwich ☐ an extra-large ☐ dancing
saw	☐ a programme ☐ to go ☐ a film ☐ an opera ☐ careful ☐ the football
got	☐ flu ☐ listen ☐ a birthday present ☐ two friends ☐ an operation
had	☐ a bath ☐ home ☐ dinner ☐ some food ☐ a drink ☐ to the kitchen
was / were	☐ tired ☐ to bed ☐ angry ☐ lunch ☐ late ☐ early ☐ cloudy

KEY: Word games

International words

Student's own answers

Alphabet

Student's own answers

Films (1)

1 The English Patient
2 From Russia With Love
3 The French Connection
4 The Mexican
5 Prince Of Egypt
6 The Boys From Brazil
7 The Italian Job
8 Congo
9 Big Trouble In Little China
10 A Passage To India
11 Zorba The Greek
12 Once Upon A Time In America

Find the words

1 name   2 his   3 nurse   4 she
5 mrs   6 he   7 number

Plurals

keys, watches, photos, dictionaries,
toothbrushes, libraries, strawberries,
armchairs, factories, pictures

Crossword

Across   1 EIGHTEEN   5 SIR   6 AM
7 MY   9 MEN   10 YELLOW   12 THAT
Down   1 ELSE   2 GERMANY   3 TAP
4 NAME   8 SMALL   11 EAT

Songs (1)

1 She Loves You
2 I Want To Hold Your* Hand
3 From Me To You
4 All You Need Is Love
5 In My* Life
6 And I Love Her
7 Please Please Me
8 All My* Loving
9 Can't Buy Me Love
10 We Can Work It Out
11 I Want You

12 I Feel Fine
13 With A Little Help From My* friends
14 When I'm Sixty-four
15 She's Leaving Home
16 You Can't Do That
17 She's A Woman
18 Two Of Us
19 I'm So Tired
20 Martha, My* Dear

Food and drink

Food: chicken, fries, pasta, burger, hot dog,
cheese, salad, fish, orange, pizza.
Drink: tea, cola, water, milk, coffee,
milkshake, juice.

Opposites: adjectives

good / bad, small / large, black / white,
old / new, left / right, open / closed,
awful / fantastic, hot / cold

Films (2)

1 Pretty Woman (**F**)   2 Three Kings (**M**)
3 Uncle (**M**) Buck   4 Sister Act (**F**)
5 Tank Girl (**F**)   6 The Lost Boys (**M**)
7 The African Queen (**F**)
8 The Godfather (**M**)   9 Men (**M**) In Black
10 Batman (**M**) Forever

Which word?

Student's own answers

Songs (2)

1 What's (**1**) Happening Brother?
2 It's (**1**) Only Rock 'n' Roll
3 She's (**2**) Got Rhythm
4 She's (**1**) Electric
5 Money's (**1**) Too tight
6 Maggie's (**3**) Farm
7 She's (**2**) Got It
8 Sylvia's (**3**) Mother
9 He's (**2**) Got The Whole World (In His Hands)
10 Who's (**1**) That Girl?

How many words (1)

telephone (9), phone, no, not, the, then, top,
note, hot, hotel, ten, open, help, let, pen

Clothes

Student's own answers

Opposites: prepositions

in / out, up / down, on / off,
to / from, along / across

Jobs

police officer, office worker
shop assistant, flight attendant
disc jockey, newspaper reporter

Odd one out (1)

shirt, new, grandson, office, flat, park,
soft drinks

Opposites: verbs

pull / push, start / finish,
turn on / turn off, come / go,
work / play, love / hate,
go out / stay in, get up / go to bed

The next word ... (1)

listen: X – the TV, for you
read: X – my, happy
write: X – a computer
turn on: X – the book, by the window
sit: X – careful
be: X – listen, me

Places

railway station   public toilet   town hall
shopping mall   taxi rank   telephone box

Sports

soccer, swimming, basketball, running,
squash, baseball, tennis, rugby, karate, golf,
football, netball

Odd one out (2)

writing, reading, Spain, can, they,
concert, film

The next word ... (2)

have: X – a film, a hospital
go: X – a pizza, a station
work: X – a meal, a bath
live in: X – breakfast, a bed
know: X – a passport
meet: X – a new car, tickets, a film

Films (3)

1 The (Third) Man   2 The (Sixth) Sense
3 The (Fifth) Element
4 Twelve Angry Men
5 The Seven Samurai
6 One Hundred And One Dalmatians
7 Six Days, Seven Nights
8 The Three Musketeers
9 The (First) Family
10 Four Weddings And A Funeral

How many words? (2)

milkshake (9), milk, a, as, is, am, he, she,
me, same, ham, like, likes, him, his, mile,
smile, hi, ski, male, has, make, sale

The next word ... (3)

see: X – lunch
make: X – an exercise, football
stay: X – a CD, the video
play: X – exercise, gymnastics, dancing
do: X – likes, clothes, a new car
have: X – working

How many words (3)

Wednesday (9), a, an, and, we, see, sees,
new, news, day, days, was, yes, saw, say,
says, way, ways, need, sad

Odd one out (3)

plane, weather, station, like, shirt, potato,
coffee

Buildings

1 office
2 farm
3 restaurant
4 hotel
5 house
6 bridge
7 church
8 cinema
9 building

The next word ... (4)

went: X – a new jacket, some fries
bought: X – to work, dancing
saw: X – to go, careful
got: X – listen, an operation
had: X – home, to the kitchen
was/were: X – to bed, lunch

Words to remember

in
English

**This is a selection of key words from Units 1–30.
You can write translations here.**

Unit 1

goodbye ....

hello ....

hi ....

name ....

number ....

telephone ....

Good to meet you. ....

I don't know ....

Unit 2

cleaner ....

doctor ....

job ....

journalist ....

nurse ....

receptionist ....

right ....

scientist ....

shop assistant ....

waiter ....

wrong ....

Unit 3

architect ....

e-mail ....

engineer ....

family name ....

first name ....

information ....

married ....

message ....

office worker ....

single ....

Unit 4

fine ....

good afternoon ....

good evening ....

good morning ....

good night ....

madam ....

problem ....

sir ....

sorry ....

speak ....

thanks ....

understand ....

Unit 5

apple ....
backpack ....
camera ....
dictionary ....
envelope ....
film ....
hat ....
identity card ....
key ....
map ....
orange ....
passport ....
pen ....
penknife ....
ticket ....
toothbrush ....
towel ....
umbrella ....
watch ....

Unit 6

busy ....
coffee ....
door ....
friend ....
holiday ....
(in a) hurry ....
menu ....
minute ....

please ....
pub ....
restaurant ....
tea ....
window ....

Unit 7

chicken ....
chocolate ....
eat ....
drink ....
fish ....
fries ....
juice ....
large ....
milk ....
milkshake ....
pepper ....
regular ....
salad ....
salt ....
strawberry ....
sugar ....
take out ....
water ....

Unit 8

angry ....

big ....

black ....

blue ....

brown ....

car ....

cold ....

colour ....

green ....

grey ....

happy ....

hot ....

lines ....

new ....

old ....

pink ....

printer ....

red ....

small ....

tap ....

unhappy ....

white ....

yellow ....

Unit 9

armchair ....

bath ....

bathrobe ....

bathroom ....

beautiful ....

bed ....

bedroom ....

carpet ....

lights ....

picture ....

room ....

shower ....

tired ....

wall ....

Unit 10

boots ....

clothes ....

dark (blue) ....

dress ....

extra (large) ....

jacket ....

light (blue) ....

medium ....

men ....

purple ....

shirt ....

shoes ....

shorts ....

size ....

skirt ....

sweatshirt ....

T-shirt ....

top ....

trainers ....

trousers ....

women ....

Unit 11

calculator ....

comb ....

credit card ....

driving licence ....

landing card ....

matches ....

paper hankies ....

stamp ....

sunglasses ....

sweets ....

Unit 12

aunt ....

baby ....

brother ....

child, children ....

cousin ....

daughter ....

father ....

grand(father) ....

husband ....

mother ....

niece ....

nephew ....

parent ....

popular ....

sister ....

son ....

uncle ....

wife ....

Unit 13

angry ....

careful ....

close ....

come ....

comic ....

forget ....

give ....

go ....

look ....

lunch ....

open ....

quiet ....

say ....

sit down ....

stand up ....

stop ....

turn off ....

turn on ....

Unit 14

bank ....

city ....

college ....

company (= plc) ....

dog ....

factory ....

flat (= apartment) ....

home ....

hospital ....

house ....

live (*verb*) ....

party ....

work ....

Unit 15

government ....

hour ....

information ....

library ....

post office ....

shop ....

superstore ....

time ....

tourist ....

weekday ....

weekend ....

Unit 16

across ....

along ....

bridge ....

bus ....

church ....

directions ....

end ....

left ....

past (the bank) ....

railway ....

right (*opposite*: left) ....

route ....

station ....

stranger ....

traffic lights ....

turn (right) ....

underground ....

Unit 17

break (coffee break) ....

breakfast ....

club ....

dinner ....

every day ....

finish ....

get up ....

go to bed ....

kitchen ....

living room ....

magazine ....

midnight ....

partner ....

snack ....

start ....

study ....

watch (TV) ....

Unit 18

blanket ....

cake ....

flight ....

fruit ....

ham ....

honeymoon ....

ice-cream ....

main course ....

newspaper ....

pillow ....

rice ....

salmon ....

seat ....

starter ....

vegetarian ....

wine ....

Unit 19

chess ....

count ....

difficult ....

drive ....

easy ....

guitar ....

prize ....

sing ....

swim ....

use (a computer) ....

whistle ....

Unit 20

appointment ....

because ....

birthday ....

date ....

early ....

free ....

late ....

next (week) ....

on time ....

tomorrow ....

Unit 21

at the moment ....

boyfriend ....

favourite ....

girlfriend ....

neighbours ....

plane ....

sleep ....

shop (verb) ....

take off ....

tennis ....

video ....

Unit 22

cut ....

diary ....

flu ....

go out ....

hair ....

hairdresser ....

operation ....

plans ....

sneeze ....

stay in ....

summer ....

sympathetic ....

vet ....

visit ....

Unit 23

ballet ....

classical ....

concert ....

diet (on a diet) ....

(football) match ....

hall (concert hall) ....

like ....

music ....

opera ....

play (at a theatre) ....

theatre ....

Unit 24

basketball ....

clean ....

cook ....

dancing ....

dislike ....

gymnastics ....

hate ....

love ....

martial arts ....

Unit 25

buy ....

die ....

fall in love ....

get married ....

jump ....

have a baby ....

leave ....

lottery ....

national ....

rain ....

sink (ship) ....

star (film star) ....

win ....

Unit 26

drawer ....

glasses ....

happy ....

pocket ....

second-hand ....

shelf ....

under ....

unhappy ....

wastebin ....

yesterday ....

Unit 27

Autumn (Fall) ....

awful ....

bag ....

beach ....

camping ....

chauffeur ....

cloudy ....

country (*opposite*: town) ....

degree (5° C) ....

journey ....

mountains ....

raining ....

season ....

snowing ....

Spring ....

Summer ....

sunny ....

temperature ....

train ....

village ....

weather ....

windy ....

Winter ....

world ....

Unit 28

bread ....

crisps ....

fridge ....

haircut ....

interview ....

lawyer ....

luck ....

manager ....

meal ....

nuts ....

pair ....

socks ....

toast ....

Unit 29

advert ....

bill ....

coat ....

frozen ....

last (night) ....

letters ....

organic ....

post ....

postcard ....

receipt ....

see ....

sell ....

Unit 30

ago ....

was born ....

famous ....

mathematics ....

move ....

pass (a test) ....

physics ....

Picture dictionary

Numbers

1 one	30 thirty
2 two	40 forty
3 three	50 fifty
4 four	60 sixty
5 five	70 seventy
6 six	80 eighty
7 seven	90 ninety
8 eight	100 one hundred / a hundred

9 nine
10 ten
11 eleven
12 twelve
13 thirteen
14 fourteen
15 fifteen
16 sixteen
17 seventeen
18 eighteen
19 nineteen

101 one hundred and one
147 one hundred and forty-seven
859 eight hundred and fifty-nine

20 twenty
21 twenty-one
22 twenty-two
23 twenty-three
24 twenty-four
25 twenty-five
26 twenty-six
27 twenty-seven
28 twenty-eight
29 twenty-nine

1000 one thousand
5,000 five thousand
10,000 ten thousand
100,000 one hundred thousand
1,000,000 one million

0 zero, 'o', nought

Days, dates

Days of the week
Monday
Tuesday
Wednesday
Thursday
Friday
Saturday
Sunday

Months of the year
January
February
March
April
May
June
July
August
September
October
November
December

Years

1900	nineteen hundred
1905	nineteen hundred and five / nineteen 'oh' five
1998	nineteen ninety-eight
2000	two thousand
2001	two thousand and one
2007	two thousand and seven
2012	twenty twelve

Ordinal numbers for dates

1st	first	11th	eleventh	21st	twenty-first
2nd	second	12th	twelfth	22nd	twenty-second
3rd	third	13th	thirteenth	23rd	twenty-third
4th	fourth	14th	fourteenth	24th	twenty-fourth
5th	fifth	15th	fifteenth	25th	twenty-fifth
6th	sixth	16th	sixteenth	26th	twenty-sixth
7th	seventh	17th	seventeenth	27th	twenty-seventh
8th	eighth	18th	eighteenth	28th	twenty-eighth
9th	ninth	19th	nineteenth	29th	twenty-ninth
10th	tenth	20th	twentieth	30th	thirtieth
				31st	thirty-first

Countries, nationalities

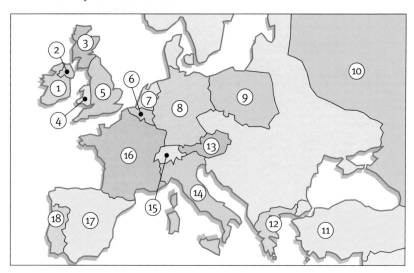

Money

| coin | note | credit card |

United Kingdom
One pound = 100 pence
Coins: 1p, 5p, 10p, 20p, 50p (one 'p', five 'p', etc), £1, £2
Notes: £5, £10, £20, £50

European Union
One euro = 100 cents
Coins: 1 cent, 2 cents, 5 cents, 10 cents,
20 cents, 50 cents, 1 euro, 2 euros
Notes: €5, €10, €20,
€50, €100, €200, €500

United States of America, Canada, Australia
One dollar = 100 cents

Coins: 1¢ (penny), 5¢ (nickel), 10¢ (dime), 25¢ (quarter)
Notes: $1, 5$, $10, $20, $50, $100

Australian dollar   Canadian dollar   American dollar

$1.25   one dollar twenty-five
$125   one hundred and twenty-five dollars
£1.25   one pound twenty-five
$2.39   two dollars thirty-nine cents
£2.39   two pounds thirty-nine

$1.50 / £1.50 = one dollar fifty / one pound fifty
(NOT one and a half dollars / pounds)

Food (1)

Fruit and vegetables

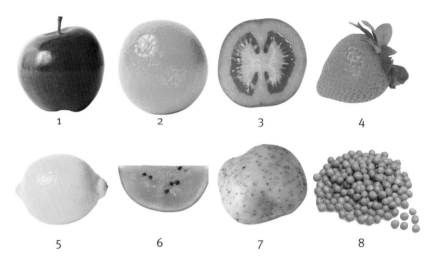

1

2

3

4

5

6

7

8

Snacks

9

10

11

12

13

On the table

14

15

16

17

Food (2)

1

2

3

4

5

6

7

8

9

10

11

12

13

14

15

16

Drinks

1

2

3

4

5

6

7

8

9

10

11

12

13

14

Rooms, furniture

1

2

3

4

5

6

7

8

9

10

11

12

13

14

15

16

Clothes

Possessions

1
2
3
4
5
6
7
8
9
10
11
12
13
14
15
16
17

Families

Key

- MALE
- FEMALE
- MALE OR FEMALE

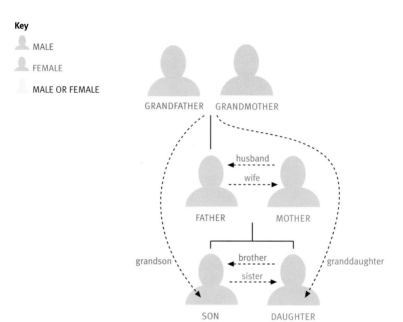

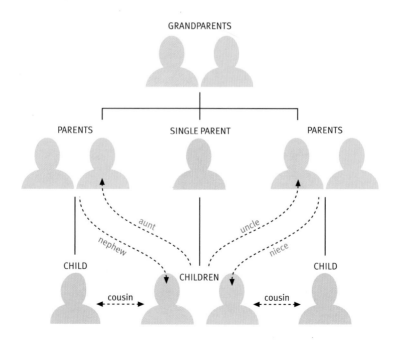

People

1 2 3 4 5

The body

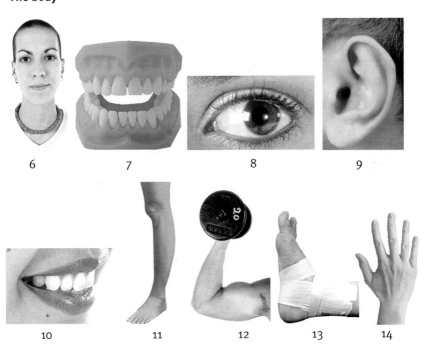

6 7 8 9

10 11 12 13 14

Buildings, places

1

2

3

4

5

6

7

8

9

10

11

Occupations

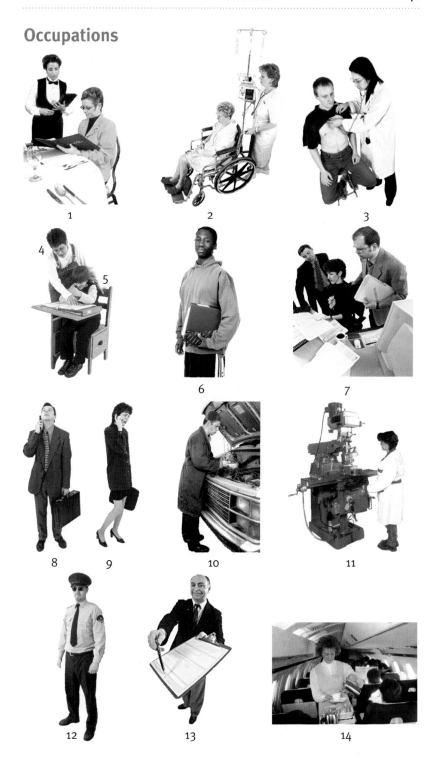

1

2

3

4

5

6

7

8　9

10

11

12

13

14

Transport

1

2

3

4

5

6

7

8

9

10

11

12

13

Computers

1

2

3

4

5

6

7

8

9

10

11

12

13

14

Sport, exercise

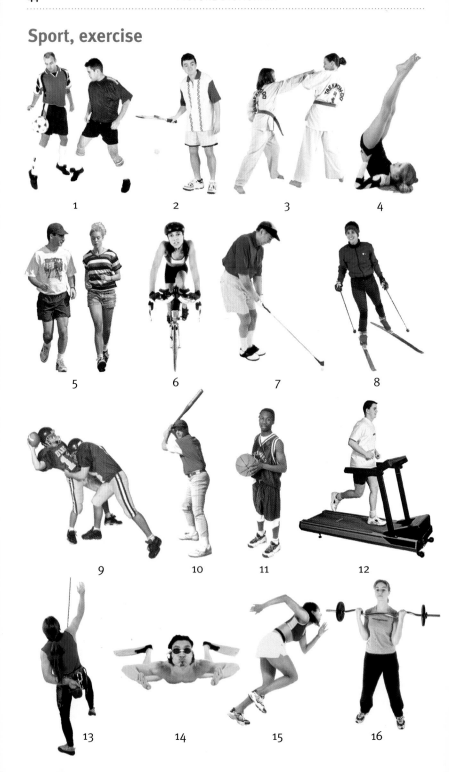

1

2

3

4

5

6

7

8

9

10

11

12

13

14

15

16

On the table

1
2
3
4
5
6
7
8
9
10
11
12
13
14
15

Appliances, bathroom

1

2

3

4

5

6

7

8

9

10

11

12

13

Leisure

1

2

3

4

5

6

7

8

9

10

11

12

Signs

1

2

3

4

5

6

7

8

9

10

11

12

13

14

15

16

17

18

19

20

KEY: Picture dictionary

The words in blue are in the International Phonetic Alphabet. There are 26 letters in the English alphabet, but there are 46 sounds.

Sounds

Vowels

iː	see	/siː/	ʌ	cup	/kʌp/
i	happy	/'hæpi/	ɜː	third	/θɜːd/
ɪ	sit	/sɪt/	ə	about	/ə'baʊt/
e	ten	/ten/	eɪ	day	/deɪ/
æ	hat	/hæt/	əʊ	go	/gəʊ/
ɑː	father	/'fɑːðə(r)/	aɪ	five	/faɪv/
ɒ	got	/gɒt/	aʊ	now	/naʊ/
ɔː	four	/fɔː(r)/	ɔɪ	boy	/bɔɪ/
ʊ	foot	/fʊt/	ɪə	near	/nɪə(r)/
u	situation	/sɪtʃu'eɪʃn/	eə	pair	/peə(r)/
uː	too	/tuː/	ʊə	tourist	/'tʊərɪst/

Consonants

p	pen	/pen/	s	so	/səʊ/
b	bad	/bæd/	z	zoo	/zuː/
t	tea	/tiː/	ʃ	shoe	/ʃuː/
d	do	/duː/	ʒ	television	/telɪ'vɪʒn/
k	cat	/kæt/	h	had	/hæd/
g	got	/gɒt/	m	man	/mæn/
tʃ	chair	/tʃeə(r)/	n	no	/nəʊ/
dʒ	June	/dʒuːn/	ŋ	sing	/sɪŋ/
f	five	/faɪv/	l	left	/left/
v	van	/væn/	r	red	/red/
θ	thank	/θæŋk/	j	yes	/jes/
ð	this	/ðɪs/	w	we	/wiː/

Numbers (no key)

Days, dates (no key)

Countries, nationalities

1 Republic of Ireland / Irish
/'aɪələnd/ /'aɪərɪʃ/

2 Northern Ireland / Irish
/nɔ:ðn 'aɪələnd/ /'aɪərɪʃ/

3 Scotland / Scottish
/'skɒtlənd/ /'skɒtɪʃ/

4 Wales / Welsh
/weɪlz/ /welʃ/

5 England / English
/'ɪŋglənd/ /'ɪŋglɪʃ/
[2–5 = United Kingdom, Britain /
British /ju: naɪtɪd 'kɪŋdəm/
/'brɪtən/ /'brɪtɪʃ/]

6 Belgium / Belgian
/'beldʒəm/ /'beldʒən/

7 The Netherlands, Holland / Dutch
/ðə 'neðələndz/ /'hɒlənd/ /dʌtʃ/

8 Germany / German
/'dʒɜ:mənɪ/ /'dʒɜ:mən/

9 Poland / Polish
/'pəʊlənd/ /'pəʊlɪʃ/

10 Russia / Russian
/'rʌʃə/ /'rʌʃn/

11 Turkey / Turkish
/'tɜ:kɪ/ /'tɜ:kɪʃ/

12 Greece / Greek
/gri:s/ /gri:k/

13 Austria / Austrian
/'ɒstrɪə/ /'ɒstrɪən/

14 Italy / Italian
/'ɪtəlɪ/ /ɪ'tælɪən/

15 Switzerland / Swiss
/'swɪtsələnd/ /swɪs/

16 France / French
/frɑ:ns/ /frentʃ/

17 Spain / Spanish
/speɪn/ /'spænɪʃ/

18 Portugal / Portuguese
/'pɔ:tʃʊgl/ /pɔ:tʃʊ'gi:z/

19 China / Chinese
/'tʃaɪnə/ /tʃaɪ'ni:z/

20 North Korea / North Korean
/ˌnɔ:θ kə'rɪə/ /ˌnɔ:θ kə'rɪən/

21 South Korea / South Korean
/ˌsaʊθ kə'rɪə/ /ˌsaʊθ kə'rɪən/

22 Japan / Japanese
/dʒə'pæn/ /ˌdʒæpə'ni:z/

23 Australia / Australian
/ɒ'streɪlɪə/ /ɒ'streɪlɪən/

24 Canada / Canadian
/'kænədə/ /kə'neɪdɪən/

25 The United States of America,
The U.S.A. / American
/ju: naɪtɪd steɪts əv ə'merɪkə/
/ðə ju: es 'eɪ/ /ə'merɪkən/

26 Mexico / Mexican
/'meksɪkəʊ/ /'meksɪkən/

27 Brazil / Brazilian
/brə'zɪl/ /brə'zɪlɪən/

28 Chile / Chilean
/'tʃɪlɪ/ /'tʃɪlɪən/

29 Argentina / Argentinian
/ɑːdʒən'ti:nə/ /ˌɑːdʒən'tɪnɪən/

30 Uruguay / Uruguayan
/'jʊərəgwaɪ/ /ˌjʊərə'gwaɪən/

Money (no key)

Food (1)

1 apple /'æpl/

2 orange /'ɒrɪndʒ/

3 tomato /tə'mɑːtəʊ/

4 strawberry /'strɔ:brɪ/

5 lemon /'lemən/

6 melon /'melən/

7 potato /pə'teɪtəʊ/

8 peas /pi:z/

9 toast /təʊst/

10 donut / doughnut /'dəʊnʌt/

11 chocolate cake /'tʃɒklət keɪk/

12 nachos /'nætʃəʊz/

13 popcorn /'pɒpkɔ:n/

14 butter /'bʌtə(r)/
15 sugar /'ʃʊɡə(r)/
16 pepper /'pepə(r)/
17 salt /sɔːlt, sɒlt/

Food (2)

1 burger /'bɜːɡə(r)/
2 hot dog /'hɒt dɒɡ/
3 sandwich /'sænwɪdʒ/
4 salad /'sæləd/

5 cheese /tʃiːz/
6 egg /eɡ/
7 fish /fɪʃ/
8 meat /miːt/

9 spaghetti /spə'ɡetɪ/
10 pasta /'pæstə/
11 rice /raɪs/
12 pizza /'piːtsə/

13 salmon /'sæmən/
14 ham /hæm/
15 chicken /'tʃɪkɪn/
16 fries / chips /fraɪz/ /tʃɪps/

Drinks

1 coffee / black coffee / espresso
  /'kɒfɪ/ /blæk 'kɒfɪ/ /e'spresəʊ/
2 white coffee / cappuccino
  /waɪt 'kɒfɪ/ /kæpuː'tʃiːnəʊ/
3 tea /tiː/
4 milk /mɪlk/

5 orange juice /'ɒrɪndʒ dʒuːs/
6 lemonade /lemə'neɪd/
7 cola /'kəʊlə/
8 strawberry milkshake
  /ˌstrɔːbrɪ 'mɪlkʃeɪk/

9 drinking chocolate /
  hot chocolate
  /'drɪŋkɪŋ tʃɒklət/ /hɒt 'tʃɒklət/
10 red wine /red 'waɪn/
11 white wine /waɪt 'waɪn/
12 beer /'bɪə(r)/

13 champagne /ˌʃæm'peɪn/
14 mineral water /'mɪnərəl
   ˌwɔːtə(r)/

Rooms, furniture

1 window /'wɪndəʊ/
2 door /dɔː(r)/
3 chair /tʃeə(r)/
4 table /'teɪbl/

5 double bed /'dʌbl bed/
6 single bed /'sɪŋɡl bed/
7 cupboard /'kʌbəd/
8 wardrobe /'wɔːdrəʊb/

9 sofa /'səʊfə/
10 carpet /'kɑːpɪt/
11 armchair /'ɑːmtʃeə(r)/
12 desk /desk/

13 drawer unit / chest of drawers
   /'drɔː, juːnɪt/ /ˌtʃest əv 'drɔːz/
14 light / lamp /laɪt/ /læmp/
15 clock /klɒk/
16 picture /'pɪktʃə(r)/

Clothes

1 shirt /ʃɜːt/
2 jacket /'dʒækɪt/
3 trousers /'traʊzəz/
  [2+3 = suit /suːt/]
4 dress /dres/
5 top /tɒp/
6 skirt /skɜːt/

7 coat /kəʊt/
8 T-shirt /'tiː ʃɜːt/
9 shorts /ʃɔːts/
10 undershirt (US) / vest (UK only)
   /'ʌndərʃɜːt/ /vest/
11 undershorts (US) /
   underpants (UK only)
   /'ʌndərʃɔːts/ /'ʌndəpænts/
   [10 + 11 = underwear
   /'ʌndəweə(r)/]
12 sweater /'swetə(r)/

13 tights   /taɪts/
14 shoes   /ʃuːz/
15 trainers   /'treɪnəz/
16 boots   /buːts/
17 socks   /spks/

18 belt   /belt/
19 gloves   /glʌvz/
20 hat   /hæt/
21 tie   /taɪ/

Possessions

1 wallet (US: also billfold)
   /'wɒlɪt/ /'bɪlfəʊld/
2 briefcase   /'briːfkeɪs/
3 purse   /pɜːs/
4 handbag (UK) / purse (US)
   /'hæmbæg/ /pɜːs/

5 comb   /kəʊm/
6 watch   /wɒtʃ/
7 glasses   /'glɑːsɪz/
8 sunglasses   /'sʌnglɑːsɪz/

9 key   /kiː/
10 pen   /pen/
11 notebook   /'nəʊtbʊk/
12 pencils   /'pensɪlz/
13 book   /bʊk/

14 mobile phone (UK) /
   cell phone (US)
   /ˌməʊbaɪl 'fəʊn/ /'sel fəʊn/
15 calculator   /'kælkjʊleɪtə(r)/
16 camera   /'kæmrə/
17 scissors   /'sɪzəz/

Families (no key)

People

Adults: /'ædʌlts/
1 man (*pl.* = men)   /mæn/ /men/
2 woman (*pl.* = women)
   /'wʊmən/ /'wɪmɪn/

Children: /'tʃɪldrən/
3 boy / child   /bɔɪ/ /tʃaɪld/
4 girl / child   /gɜːl/ /tʃaɪld/
5 baby   /'beɪbɪ/

The body: /'bɒdɪ/
6 head   /hed/
7 teeth   /tiːθ/
8 eye   /aɪ/
9 ear   /ɪə(r)/

10 mouth   /maʊθ/
11 leg   /leg/
12 arm   /ɑːm/
13 foot   /fʊt/
14 hand   /hænd/

Buildings, places

1 house   /haʊs/
2 flat / apartment
   /flæt/ /ə'pɑːtmənt/
3 office building   /'ɒfɪs ˌbɪldɪŋ/

4 church   /tʃɜːtʃ/
5 hotel   /həʊ'tel/
6 pub   /pʌb/

7 restaurant   /'restrɒnt/
8 cinema (US: movie theater)
   /'sɪnəmə/ /'muːvɪ ˌθiːətər/
9 farm   /fɑːm/

10 bridge   /brɪdʒ/
11 tower   /'taʊə(r)/

Occupations

1 waiter (+ customer)
/'weɪtə(r)/ /'kʌstəmə(r)/
2 nurse (+ patient)
/nɜːs/ /'peɪʃənt/
3 doctor /'dɒktə(r)/
4 teacher /'tiːtʃə(r)/
5 pupil /'pjuːpl/
6 student /'stjuːdənt/
7 office workers /'ɒfɪs wɜːkəz/
8 businessman /'bɪznɪsmən/
9 businesswoman
/'bɪznɪswʊmən/
10 mechanic /mə'kænɪk/
11 factory worker /'fæktrɪ
ˌwɜːkə(r)/
12 police officer /pə'liːs ɒfɪsə(r)/
13 salesperson, salesman
/'seɪlzpɜːsən/ /'seɪlzmən/
14 flight attendant
/'flaɪt əˌtendənt/

Transport

1 car /kɑː(r)/
2 van (US: panel truck)
/væn/ /'pænl trʌk/
3 bus /bʌs/
4 truck (UK only; lorry)
/trʌk/ /'lɒrɪ/
5 four-wheel drive
(US: utility vehicle)
/fɔː wiːl 'draɪv/ /juː'tɪlətiː ˌviːəkl/
6 MPV / People carrier
(US: van, mini-van)
/ˌem piː 'viː/ /'piːpl ˌkærɪə(r)/
7 ambulance /'æmbjuːləns/
8 motorbike /'məʊtəbaɪk/
9 bike / bicycle /baɪk/ /'baɪsɪkl/
10 train /treɪn/
11 plane /pleɪn/

12 ship /ʃɪp/
13 boat /bəʊt/

Computers

1 laptop (computer)
/ˌlæptɒp kəm'pjuːtə(r)/
2 computer /kəm'pjuːtə(r)/
3 monitor /'mɒnɪtə(r)/
4 keyboard /'kiːbɔːd/
5 key /kiː/
6 mouse /maʊs/
7 joystick /'dʒɔɪstɪk/
8 modem /'məʊdem/
9 disk drive /'dɪsk draɪv/
10 CD (compact disc), CD-ROM, DVD
/siː 'diː/ /siː diː 'rɒm/
/diː viː 'diː/
11 disks (floppy disks) /dɪsks/
12 printer /'prɪntə(r)/
13 scanner /'skænə(r)/
14 cable, connector
/'keɪbl/ /kə'nektə(r)/

Sport, exercise

1 football, playing football
(US: soccer) /'fʊtbɔːl/ /'sɒkər/
2 tennis, playing tennis /'tenɪs/
3 martial arts (this is taekwondo)
/ˌmɑːʃl 'ɑːts/
4 gymnastics /dʒɪm'næstɪks/
5 jogging /'dʒɒgɪŋ/
6 cycling, riding a bicycle
/'saɪklɪŋ/
7 golf, playing golf /gɒlf/
8 skiing /'skiːɪŋ/
9 American football,
playing American football
/əˌmerɪkən 'fʊtbɔːl/
10 baseball, playing baseball
/'beɪsbɔːl/

11 basketball, playing basketball
/'bɑːskɪtbɔːl/
12 exercising, taking exercise
/'eksəsaɪzɪŋ/

13 climbing   /'klaɪmɪŋ/
14 swimming   /'swɪmɪŋ/
15 running   /'rʌnɪŋ/
16 weight-training   /'weɪtˌtreɪnɪŋ/

On the table

1 fork   /fɔːk/
2 plate   /pleɪt/
3 knife   /naɪf/
4 bowl   /bəʊl/
5 spoon   /spuːn/

6 cup   /kʌp/
7 saucer   /'sɔːsə(r)/
8 mug   /mʌg/
9 glass   /glɑːs/

10 bottle   /'bɒtl/
11 jug   /dʒʌg/
12 teapot   /'tiːpɒt/

13 coffee pot   /'kɒfiː pɒt/
14 tray   /treɪ/
15 napkin   /'næpkɪn/

Appliances, bathroom

Kitchen:
1 microwave   /'maɪkrəʊweɪv/
2 cooker   /'kʊkə(r)/
3 washing machine
/'wɒʃɪŋ məˌʃiːn/
4 fridge   /frɪdʒ/

Bathroom:
5 toilet   /'tɔɪlət/
6 bath   /bɑːθ/
7 shower   /'ʃaʊə(r)/
8 taps   /tæps/

TV, etc:
9 televison, TV   /telə'vɪʒn/ /tiː 'viː/

10 remote, remote control
/rɪˌməʊt kən'trəʊl/
11 video (UK) / VCR (US).
Also DVD, DVD player
/ˌvɪdɪəʊ/ /viː siː 'ɑːr/
/diː viː diː 'pleɪə(r)/
12 radio, radio-cassette
/'reɪdɪəʊ/ /'reɪdɪəʊ kə'set/
13 stereo, hi-fi   /'sterɪəʊ/ /'haɪ faɪ/

Leisure

1 dancing   /'dɑːnsɪŋ/
2 watching TV   /wɒtʃɪŋ tiː 'viː/
3 eating out / being with friends
/ˌiːtɪŋ 'aʊt/ /ˌbiːɪŋ wɪð 'frendz/

4 walking   /'wɔːkɪŋ/
5 camping   /'kæmpɪŋ/
6 shopping   /'ʃɒpɪŋ/

7 going to the cinema / theatre
/ˌgəʊɪŋ tə ðə 'sɪnəmə, 'θiːətə(r)/
8 reading   /'riːdɪŋ/
9 playing (chess)   /'pleɪɪŋ 'tʃes/

10 cooking   /'kʊkɪŋ/
11 collecting things
/kə'lektɪŋ θɪŋz/
12 surfing the internet
/ˌsɜːfɪŋ ðiː 'ɪntənet/

Signs

1 motorway   /'məʊtəweɪ/
7 car park   /'kɑː pɑːk/
9 telephone   /'teləfəʊn/
10 toilets   /'tɔɪləts/
16 No smoking. / Don't smoke.
/ˌnəʊ 'sməʊkɪŋ/ /ˌdəʊnt 'sməʊk/
20 information   /ɪnfə'meɪʃn/

Everyday English

How to use this section

Inside your *3 in 1 Practice Pack* there is a square of red plastic.
When you cover the text with this square you can read the words in black,
but you can't see the words in pink.

■ = Put the red plastic square over the conversation.

Method

1 Read the conversation.
2 ■ Put the red plastic square over the conversation.
3 Complete the conversation. Remember the words in pink.
   Say them to yourself.

Interaction with strangers

Complete the conversations.

Greetings

Complete the conversations.

Introductions

Minimum conversation

A   Hi.
B   Hi.
A   Are you a student?
B   Yes.
A   Are you English?
B   No.
A   Where are you from?
B   Canada.
A   My name's Rod. I'm Australian.
B   Oh.
A   What's your name?
B   Tina.
A   Good to meet you, Tina.

Interesting conversation

A   Hi.
B   Hi.
A   Are you a student?
B   Yes, I am. I'm in the
    English department.
A   Are you English?
B   No, I'm not. I'm Canadian.
A   Really? Where from?
B   Toronto. Where are you from?
A   Australia. My name's Rod.
B   My name's Tina.
A   Good to meet you, Tina.
B   Good to meet you, Rod.

1   ▦   **You are Tina. Complete the first conversation.**

2   ▦   **You are Tina. Complete the second conversation.**

3   ▦   **Complete the second conversation. Give true answers.**

Goodbyes

■ **Complete the conversations.**

Hotel check-in

A Good evening.
B Good evening. Can I help you?
A Yes. Can I check in please?
B Yes, sir. What's your name?
A Carter. David Carter.
B Can you spell that?
A Yes. C-A-R-T-E-R. Carter.
B Thank you. What's your home address?
A 45, Clarendon Street, Oxford.
B Can you spell 'Clarendon', please?
A C-L-A-R-E-N-D-O-N.
B What's your phone number?
A 01865-098372
B Thank you. Room 15. Here's your key.
A Thank you.
B You're welcome.

■ **You are the hotel receptionist. Complete the conversation.**

A Good afternoon.
B Good afternoon.
A Can I check in, please?
B Of course. Name?
A My name's (give your name).
B Can you repeat that?
A (Give your name.)
B I'm sorry. Can you spell it?
A (Spell your name.)
B And your address?
A (Give your address.)
B And your phone number?
A (Give your phone number.)
B OK. This is your key. Room 13.
A Thank you.

■ **You are the hotel guest.
Give true answers.**

Problems

■ **Complete the conversations.**

Telephoning

A AGT International. Good morning.
B Good morning. Is Ms Baker in?
A I'm sorry. She's out. Can her secretary help you?
B Yes. Can I speak to her secretary, please?
A Certainly. What's your name?
B Anna Green.
A Thank you. Just a minute.

■ **You are Anna Green.**
Complete the conversation.

A Hello?
B Is that 01202-051798?
A Yes, it is.
B Are you Mrs Cook?
A Yes, I am.
B Good afternoon, Mrs Cook. I'm from International Surveys plc.
   Can I ask you some questions?
A No, I'm sorry. I'm busy.
B Can I phone you this evening?
A No, I'm sorry. Goodbye.

■ **You are Mrs Cook. Complete the conversation.**

Fast food

Next ...

Here you are.

A coffee, please.

Thanks.

A burger, please.

Anything else?

No, thanks.

There you go.

And a chocolate milkshake, please.

Regular or large?

Large, please.

Here you are.

A cheeseburger, please.

With fries?

Yes, please.

Anything to drink?

No, thanks.

■ **Complete the conversations.**

Shopping

A Can I help you?
B Yes. I'm looking for a T-shirt.
A What colour?
B Light blue.
A What size?
B Extra large.
A Here you are.
B Thank you. How much is it?
A Twenty-nine pounds ninety-nine.
B Thanks. Where's the cash desk?
A It's over there.
B Thank you.
A You're welcome.

▦ **You are the shop assistant.
Complete the conversation.**

A Can I help you?
B I'm looking for a teapot.
A What colour?
B Brown, please.
A Large or small?
B Small, please.
A Is this one OK?
B Yes. That's fine. How much is it?
A Twelve pounds forty-nine.

▦ **You are the customer. Complete the conversation.**

Restaurant

■ **Complete the conversations.**

Being a good listener

A   I've got a new car.
B   Really?
A   Yes. It's a BMW sports car.
B   That's nice.
A   It's got a CD player.
B   Great.
A   And it's got a cassette player.
B   That's good.
A   Would you like a ride?
B   Yeah. OK.

▦ **You are the listener. Complete the conversation.**

A   There's a good pub in Shipley.
B   Is there?
A   Yes, it's in the town centre.
B   Right.
A   It's next to the bank.
B   Oh, yes?
A   In Market Street. Near the town hall.
B   Uh-huh.
A   It's called the Red Lion.
B   The Red Lion?
A   Right. It's very old.
B   Uh-huh.
A   Oh, yes. It's got three bars
    and a restaurant.
B   A restaurant?
A   Yes, an excellent restaurant.

▦ **You are the listener.**
Complete the
conversation.

Introducing people

■ **Complete the conversations.**

Asking for directions

■ **Complete the conversations.**

Opening and closing times

A   Excuse me, do you live here?
B   Yes, I do.
A   When does the information office open?
B   I'm sorry. I don't know.

A   When does the bank open?
B   At nine thirty.
A   When does it close?
B   At four o'clock.
A   What's the time now?
B   It's eight forty-five.

A   What time do the shops open?
B   At nine.
A   When do they close?
B   Five thirty or six.
A   Thanks.

A   Is the tourist office open today?
B   No, it isn't. It's closed on Mondays.

■ **Complete the conversations.**

Requests

■ **Complete the conversations.**

Offers

Making offers

A   Would you like a drink?
B   Yes, please.
A   Tea or coffee?
B   Tea, please.
A   Would you like milk and sugar?
B   Milk, no sugar.
A   Have a biscuit.
B   No, thanks.
A   Go on.
B   Oh, all right. Thanks.

Accepting and refusing offers

A   Would you like a drink?
B   Yes, please.
A   Hot or cold?
B   Oh, I'd love a cold drink.
A   What about a lemonade?
B   Have you got anything else?
A   Yes. Cola, milk or mineral water.
B   Cola, please.
A   Would you like ice?
B   No, thanks.

■ **Complete the conversations.**

Seats

Complete the conversations.

Arrangements

Complete the conversations.

After a meal

A Excuse me ...
B Yes, madam?
A Can we have the bill, please?
B Here you are. Was everything all right?
A Yes. It was very nice, thank you.
B Good.
A Is service included?
B Yes, it is.
A Do you take credit cards?
B Yes, of course.

▧ **You are the customer.
Complete the conversation.**

A Did you enjoy your meal?
B Yes, very much. Can we have our coats, please?
A Yes, I've got them here.
B Thank you.
A Thank you, madam. Please come again.

▧ **You are the waiter. Complete the conversation.**

Suggestions

■ **Complete the conversations.**

Test yourself

in
English

How to use this section

**Inside your *3 in 1 Practice Pack* there is a square of red plastic.
When you cover the text with this square you can read the words in black,
but you can't see the words in pink.**

PINK
BLACK

PI
BLACK

Method

1 Cover the test with the red plastic square. You can see the words in black.
   You can't see the words in pink.
2 Remember the words in pink. Say them to yourself.
3 Do the tests after Units 5, 10, 15, 20, 25 and 30 of the Student's Book.
   Do the tests again a week later.

Test 1 (Units 1–5)

1   My name's Paul. I'm a student.

2   Can you spell your name, please?

3   Where are you from?

4   I'm from Australia. I'm Australian.

5   'Where's Glasgow?' 'It's in Scotland.'

6   'Where's Stirling?' 'I'm sorry. I don't know.'

7   'Do you speak Spanish?' 'No, I don't.'

8   She's an office worker.

9   'Are they your books?' 'Yes, they're my books.'

10 'My name's Tom.' 'Hello, Tom. Good to meet you!'

11 'What are they?' 'They're car keys.'

12 Sorry. Can you repeat it?

13 'How are you?' 'Fine, thanks. And you?'

14 His name's David, and her name's Maria.

15 'Excuse me, are you a student?'

16 'Are they your pens?' 'No, they aren't.'

17 'Is she a journalist?' 'No, she isn't.'

18 'Are you English?' 'No, I'm not.'

19 'What's his job?' 'He's an engineer.'

20 I'm sorry. I don't understand the question.

Test 2 (Units 6–10)

1   Can we have the menu? We're in a hurry.

2   'Coffee?' 'Yes, please.'

3   'Are they in the office?' 'No, they aren't.'

4   'Are you and Anna friends?' 'Yes, we are.'

5   Can I have the ketchup, please?

6   'Fries and a milkshake. Anything else?' 'No, thanks.'

7   'What colour are your trainers?' 'They're blue.'

8   There aren't any towels in the bathroom.

9   There are some books on the table.

10   Good morning, sir. Can I help you?

11   I'm looking for a dark blue T-shirt.

12   How much is the jacket?

13   How much are the boots?

14   'Who is the milkshake for?' 'It's for him. The coffee's for me.'

15   There are two single beds in the room.

16   'What size is the sweatshirt?' 'It's medium.'

17   'Are there any light blue tops?' 'No, sorry.'

18   'A cola, please.' 'Regular or large?'

19   'Six fifty, please.' 'Here you are.'

20   'How much is it?' 'Eight dollars ninety-nine.'

Test 3 (Units 11–15)

1 Have you got a passport?

2 Has she got a driving licence?

3 I've got a new computer.

4 It's an old car. It hasn't got a CD player.

5 How many children have they got?

6 Sarah and Andrew are married. Andrew is Sarah's husband.

7 Please be careful!

8 Please stay. Don't go.

9 They don't live in Oxford. They live in London.

10 Where does she live?

11 What time do the shops open?

12 She works in an office, and he works in a shop.

13 The bank doesn't open on Sundays.

14 We work in London, but we don't live there.

15 When does the information office open?

16 The offices are closed at weekends.

17 Their names are Jack and Chloe.

18 They're our friends. They go to school with us.

19 'What time is it?' 'It's twelve o'clock.'

20 Do you live in London?

Test 4 (Units 16–20)

1   Excuse me, I'm looking for the bus station.

2   Can you give me directions to the post office?

3   We start work at nine, and we finish work at five.

4   What time do you have lunch?

5   'Where do you have lunch?' 'At home.'

6   I'd like some tea, please.

7   'Would you like milk and sugar in your tea?' 'Please.'

8   'Do you like chocolate?' 'Yes, but I don't eat it.'

9   Would you like this seat or that seat?

10 'Can you play the guitar?' 'No, I can't.'

11 New Year's Day is the first of January.

12 Can I see the doctor this afternoon?

13 I'd like an appointment for tomorrow morning.

14 May is the fifth month of the year.

15 When is your father's birthday?

16 I haven't got your address.

17 He can't see you today. How about tomorrow?

18 She can speak Italian, but she can't speak French.

19 Do you have breakfast at home?

20 My birthday's in July.

Test 5 (Units 21–25)

1   I'm busy. I can't speak to him at the moment.

2   'What's she doing now?' 'She's working.'

3   She can't come to the phone. She's having a bath at the moment.

4   'Let's go for a drink.' 'OK.'

5   What about going to the new café in the High Street?

6   He likes her, but she doesn't like him.

7   'Do you like playing tennis?' 'Yes, I do.'

8   'Would you like a drink now?' 'No, thanks.'

9   They love watching old films.

10 What are you going to do tomorrow?

11 'When is she going to have a baby?' 'In January.'

12 Is it going to rain tomorrow?

13 They like us, but we don't like them.

14 'Do you like jazz?' 'No, I don't.'

15 'Would you like a sandwich?' 'No, I wouldn't.'

16 'Are you staying in this weekend?' 'Yes, I am.'

17 British children don't go to school in August.

18 Where are you going on holiday?

19 'Let's get some popcorn.' 'OK.'

20 They're going to get married in April.

Test 6 (Units 26–30)

1 It was hot yesterday.

2 'Where were you yesterday?' 'I was at a party.'

3 'Were they here last week?' 'No, they weren't.'

4 'It's raining today.' 'Yes, it was raining last night too.'

5 'What was the weather like?' 'It was cloudy.'

6 'How was your journey?' 'Not bad.'

7 We had pizza for dinner last night.

8 We had dinner at seven o'clock yesterday evening.

9 Did you have a good time at the party?

10 What did you have for lunch?

11 'Did you go out last night?' 'No, I didn't.'

12 'Did you go to the cinema?' 'Yes, I did.'

13 'What film did you see?' '*Star Wars* Episode III.'

14 I saw a good TV programme last night.

15 My grandmother's Irish. She was born in Ireland.

16 'Did you buy anything yesterday?' 'Yes, I bought a DVD.'

17 We lived in Wales for ten years.

18 Did you study English at school?

19 'This is a no smoking area.' 'I'm sorry. I didn't know.'

20 Where were you born?

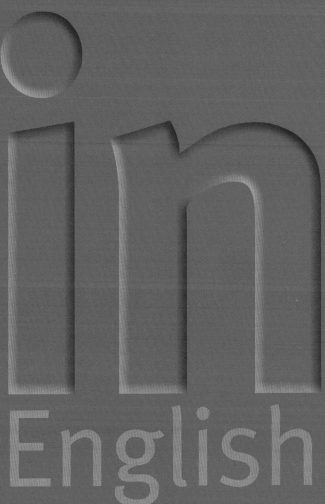

Reading for pleasure

in
English

An e-mail romance

From: Jill Bates.jillb@abc.uk.com
To: Steve Dobbs.steved@abc.uk.com
Time: 9.05 a.m.

Steve -
Hi. How are you?

From: Steve Dobbs.steved@abc.uk.com
To: Jill Bates.jillb@abc.uk.com
Time: 9.10 a.m.

Hey, Jill -
I'm very well, thanks. And you?

From: Jill Bates.jillb@abc.uk.com
To: Steve Dobbs.steved@abc.uk.com
Time: 9.15 a.m.

Steve -
I'm fine. Are you busy?

From: Steve Dobbs.steved@abc.uk.com
To: Jill Bates.jillb@abc.uk.com
Time: 9.30 a.m.

Jill -
I'm very busy. :-)
See you at 12?

From: Jill Bates.jillb@abc.uk.com
To: Steve Dobbs.steved@abc.uk.com
Time: 9.35 a.m.

Steve -
OK. 12. Carnaby Café?

From: Steve Dobbs.steved@abc.uk.com
To: Jill Bates.jillb@abc.uk.com
Time: 9.40 a.m.

Jill -
OK. See you. Bye for now.

From: Jill Bates.jillb@abc.uk.com
To: Steve Dobbs.steved@abc.uk.com
Time: 9.45 a.m.

Steve -
Bye. xxx

A postcard from Wales

Dear Dave and Anna,
We're in Wales. I'm in a
café. I'm by the window.
The café is by the sea
and it's beautiful. Bill
isn't here. He's in a pub.
We're very busy here. Do
you speak Welsh?
We don't. We don't
understand anything!
See you,

Sarah (& Bill)

(Sorry, we don't know
your postcode).

Name: Mr and Mrs Blair

Street: 13 Thatcher Street

City: Liverpool

Postcode: ???

Llanfairpwllgwyngyllgogerychwyrndrobwll-llantysiliogogogoch, Snowdonia, North Wales

See you in 20 years ...

POST CARD

Dear Mum,

My room is very small. The
walls are grey. There's a bed,
and there's a table and a
chair. There aren't any
pictures on the wall. There
isn't a TV. There are some old
books. There's a plate and a
spoon, but there aren't any
knives and forks.

See you in 20 years,

Love,

Pete (#23987654221)

Mrs Robina Banks
33 Midland Road
Westminster
London
W1A 4WW

Geography and colours

Where are the places in the box? Do you know? Test a friend!

The White Sea	China
The Blue Mountains	Texas, USA
The Black Mountains	Russia
The Yellow River	Egypt
The Red Sea	Russia
The Black Sea	Germany
The Red River	Kentucky, USA
The Black Forest	Wales

Family names

The top-ten family names in the London Telephone Directory are:

1   Smith
2   Brown
3   Jones
4   Williams, Williamson
5   Clark, Clarke

6   Harris, Harrison
7   Taylor
8   Roberts, Robertson
9   Patel
10 James

What have they got?

Angelica Unverhau from Germany has got 168,700 different pens from 137 different countries.

Jason Joiner from London has got 20,000 Star Wars toys.

William Christensen from the USA has got 75,000 different beer cans.

Tony Mattia from Brighton, England has got 1,125 Barbie dolls. He has got only 50% of the Barbie doll models made since 1959.

Claive Vadiz of Brazil has got 2,571 different bottles of whisky. They are all full. Edoardo Giaccone from Italy had 5,502 different bottles of whisky, but he died in 1997.

Michel Pont from France has got 100 jet fighter planes. He has got 70 different types. He's also got 500 motorcycles.

Fiorenzo Barindelli from Italy has got every Swatch watch. He has got nearly 4,000 different watches. He opened a Swatch museum in 2000.

Mixed-up stories

These two texts are mixed up. Some lines from Text A are in Text B, and some lines from Text B are in Text A.
Highlight the lines about Lauren.

Text A

Lauren is an English movie star. She's married to Tom Mike and Paul. Georgia is 22, Mike is 19, and Paul is two boys. Lauren is in a new sci-fi movie about Oxford. Mike's a student in London, and Paul is a waiter. Paul's restaurant is an Italian pizzeria and it hasn't got anything to eat or drink. Tom is Italian, and is very beautiful.

Text B

Sophie has got three children. Their names are Georgia, Carter, the Hollywood director. Tom is American, and their children are at school in Los Angeles. They've got 18. Her daughter, Georgia, is a nurse at a hospital in Mars. In the movie, Lauren is an astronaut and she is in the centre of London. Paul's girlfriend, Maria, is the director of the movie.

A message

Rewrite the message with *eat*.

Where do they eat chocolate?

These are the ten countries that eat the most chocolate (per person):

1 Belgium
2 Switzerland
3 Iceland
4 Germany
5 Austria
6 The United Kingdom
7 Norway
8 France
9 Denmark
10 Italy

Waiter jokes

Customer Waiter! There's a fly in my soup!
Waiter   Don't worry. It's dead.

Customer Waiter! There's a fly in my soup!
Waiter   Don't worry. It can swim.

Customer Waiter! Your hand is in my soup!
Waiter   It's all right, madam. It isn't hot.

Customer Waiter! There's an insect in my salad!
Waiter   Shh! Be quiet. Or all the customers are going to ask for one.

Some English words from other languages

language	words
French	café, restaurant, beef, omelette, bureau
Italian	piano, pizza, pasta, violin, balcony
German	kindergarten, lager, waltz, frankfurter
Spanish	guitar, mosquito, ranch, patio, tornado
Dutch (The Netherlands)	boss, cookie, patron, Yankee
Japanese	sushi, karate, bonsai, karaoke
Greek	thermometer, telephone, psychology
Turkish	coffee, kiosk, kebab
Native American	potato, tomato, chocolate, anorak, nachos
Chinese	tea, kung fu, tycoon
Hindi (India)	shampoo, pyjamas, jungle
Australian aborigine	boomerang, kangaroo

Left or right?

In most of Europe and in the United States, cars drive on the right.
In forty-two countries, cars drive on the left. Here are ten examples:

1 United Kingdom
2 Japan
3 Australia
4 South Africa
5 India

6 Indonesia
7 Thailand
8 Malaysia
9 New Zealand
10 Nigeria

An English rhyme

Thirty days has September,
April, June and November.
All the rest have thirty-one
Except for February alone
Which has twenty-eight days clear
And twenty-nine in each leap year.

Where do tourists go?

These are the top-ten countries for tourism:

1	France	6	Austria
2	The USA	7	Britain
3	Spain	8	Mexico
4	Italy	9	Germany
5	Hungary	10	Canada

City names in English

Some cities have different names in English:

English name	Original name
Lyons	Lyon (French)
Geneva	Genève (French)
Naples	Napoli (Italian)
Rome	Roma (Italian)
Milan	Milano (Italian)
Florence	Firenze (Italian)
Corruna	La Coruña (Spanish)
Lisbon	Lisboa (Portuguese)
Athens	Athinai (Greek)
Munich	München (German)
Vienna	Wien (German)
Warsaw	Warszawa (Polish)
Moscow	Moskva (Russian)

A phone call

Little boy Yes?
Man Good morning. I'm from Acme Insurance. Who am I speaking to?
Little boy Me.
Man Ah. Can I speak to your father, please?
Little boy He isn't here.
Man Can I speak to your mother?
Little boy No. She's having a bath.
Man Is there anybody else in the house?
Little boy Yes. My sister.
Man Good. Can I speak to your sister, please?
Little boy OK.

(five minutes later)
Little boy Hello?
Man Yes?
Little boy My sister can't come to the phone. I can't get her out of her bed.
Man Oh, dear. Is she all right?
Little boy Oh, yes. But she's only six months old.

Film or movie?

In British English, people see a **film** at a **cinema**. In the USA, people see a **movie** at a **movie theater**. In the USA there are two spellings, **theatre** (the same as Britain) and **theater**. Several groups of American cinemas (AMC, Universal, Century) use the British spelling. Don't worry! You can say **movie** in Britain and **film** in the USA. People understand. Cinemas with many **screens** are **multiplexes** or **cineplexes** in the USA and Britain.

An English children's rhyme

There was a little girl
And she had a little curl
Right in the middle of her forehead
And when she was good
She was very very good
But when she was bad
She was HORRID!

Elvis

Elvis Presley died in 1977. The next day people all over the world bought twenty million Elvis records. 700,000 people visit Elvis's home, Graceland, every year. It's in Memphis, Tennessee.

Police jokes

Police officer	Excuse me, sir. You didn't stop at the red light.
Driver	I'm very sorry, officer. I didn't see it.
Police officer	What's your name?
Driver	Ulysses Eamonn Xavier Ziolkowski.
Police officer	Can you spell that? ... Oh, don't worry. Forget it. But don't do it again!

Police officer	Excuse me, sir. Can you come to the police station with me?
Man	Why? What's the problem?
Police officer	No problem. But I don't like walking in the dark on my own.

Police officer	Why are you in prison?
Prisoner	Because of photography.
Police officer	Why? What's wrong with taking photographs?
Prisoner	I didn't take photographs. I took cameras.

Journalist	Do you like your job?
Police officer	Like it? I love it.
Journalist	Why's that?
Police officer	I was a shop assistant last year. The customer was always right. Now the customer is always wrong!

Food adverts on British TV

The top-ten foods in British TV adverts are:

1 Breakfast cereal (e.g. Cornflakes)
2 Frozen food
3 Tea
4 Sauces and ketchups
5 Instant coffee
6 Potato crisps and snacks
7 Ice-cream
8 Margarine
9 Cheese
10 Milk and butter

Old names / new names

Some cities have now got different names.

New York was a Dutch town. The old name was New Amsterdam.
The old name for Toronto was Fort York.
The old name for Chicago was Fort Dearborn.

School jokes

Teacher	What happened in 1564?
Boy	Shakespeare was born.
Teacher	Very good. And what happened in 1588?
Boy	Uh … Shakepeare was twenty-four years old.

Teacher	The universe is very, very big. How many stars can you see at night?
Tommy	Thousands.
Teacher	No.
Anna	Millions.
Teacher	No. What do you think, Emma?
Emma	Three.
Teacher	Three? That's a very small number.
Emma	Yes, miss. But I've got a very small window in my bedroom.

Mother	What did you do at school today?
Little girl	We did writing.
Mother	That's nice. What did you write?
Little girl	I don't know. We didn't do reading.

OXFORD
UNIVERSITY PRESS

Great Clarendon Street, Oxford OX2 6DP

Oxford University Press is a department of the
University of Oxford. It furthers the University's
objective of excellence in research, scholarship,
and education by publishing worldwide in

Oxford New York

Auckland Cape Town Dar es Salaam
Hong Kong Karachi Kuala Lumpur Madrid
Melbourne Mexico City Nairobi New Delhi
Shanghai Taipei Toronto

With offices in

Argentina Austria Brazil Chile Czech Republic
France Greece Guatemala Hungary Italy Japan
Poland Portugal Singapore South Korea
Switzerland Thailand Turkey Ukraine Vietnam

OXFORD and OXFORD ENGLISH are registered
trade marks of Oxford University Press in the UK
and in certain other countries

© Oxford University Press / Three Vee Limited 2002

The moral rights of the author have been asserted

Database right Oxford University Press (maker)

First published 2002
2009 2008 2007 2006 2005
10 9 8 7 6 5 4 3

No unauthorized photocopying

All rights reserved. No part of this publication
may be reproduced, stored in a retrieval system, or
transmitted, in any form or by any means, without
the prior permission in writing of Oxford University
Press, or as expressly permitted by law, or under
terms agreed with the appropriate reprographics
rights organization. Enquiries concerning
reproduction outside the scope of the above should
be sent to the ELT Rights Department, Oxford
University Press, at the address above

You must not circulate this book in any other
binding or cover and you must impose this same
condition on any acquirer

Any websites referred to in this publication are in
the public domain and their addresses are provided
by Oxford University Press for information only.
Oxford University Press disclaims any responsibility
for the content

ISBN-13: 978 0 19 434051 9
ISBN-10: 0 19 434051 1

Typeset in Meta

Printed in China

ACKNOWLEDGEMENTS

Designed by: Richard Morris, Stonesfield Design

The Publisher and Authors would like to thank the
many teachers and institutions who piloted this
material in Brazil, China, Eire, France, Hungary,
Italy, Mexico, Poland, Spain, and the UK.

Authors' Acknowledgements:

In a complex series like this, which has taken
several years to prepare, pilot, and produce, many
people are involved and have creative input. We
wish to thank the many people at OUP who
participated in making this book. We would like to
add our further personal thanks to Catherine Smith
(Project Manager and Student's Book Editor),
Richard Morris (Designer for all components),
Debra Emmett (Editor 3 in 1 Practice Pack), and
Madeleine Williamson (Editor, Teacher's Book and
Photocopiables).

Illustrations by:

Richard Morris: pp. 30, 38

Commissioned photography by:

Steve Betts: pp. 31.4, 32.8, 34.6, 34.14, 46.7, 57
(tr, br, bl), 60 (tl), 62 (tl), 64, 65 (t), 70, 71 (bl), 73
(tl, tr, br), 74 (bl), 75 (b)
Richard Morris: pp. 31.4, 40.8
Peter Viney: p. 93

*The publishers would like to thank the following
for their kind permission to reproduce photographs:*
Hemera Technologies for all photographs except
where credited otherwise.
PhotoDisc: pp. 31.2, 31.11, 40.4, 40.6, 40.7, 40.10,
40.11, 47.7, 71 (tl), 76 (br background), 89, 92